My NATIVITY

STICKER ACTIVITY BOOK

Have fun completing this book!

Use your pencils and stickers to finish the activities on each page. There are also cute press-outs and extra stickers to use anywhere you want!

A SPECIAL VISIT

An angel visits Mary. Find the missing sticker and follow the trails to find out which one speaks to her.

Colour the flowers.

THE LONG JOURNEY

Mary and Joseph travel to Bethlehem.
Colour and sticker the scene.

TOWN TROUBLE

The pair need somewhere to stay. Follow the trail and sticker the town to find a place.

STABLE SCENES

One innkeeper offers them his stable. Circle five differences between these two scenes.

JESUS IS BORN!

Use colour and stickers to finish the stable scene. Then, search for the things on the list below. Tick them off as you find them.

- [ ] 1 manger

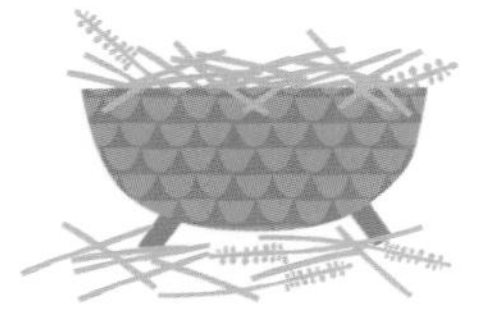

- [ ] 2 angels

- [ ] 5 mice

- [ ] 1 cow

- [ ] 1 star

- [ ] 1 donkey

- [ ] 4 sheep

SWEET DREAMS

Doodle what you think baby Jesus is dreaming about.

FAITHFUL FRIENDS

The stable animals watch over Jesus.
Draw lines to match the animal
babies to their mothers.

GOOD NEWS

An angel tells some shepherds the good news.
Trace her message.

A special baby has been born in a stable in Bethlehem. His name is Jesus.

THE SHEPHERDS' VISIT

Guide the shepherds through the maze to reach the stable.

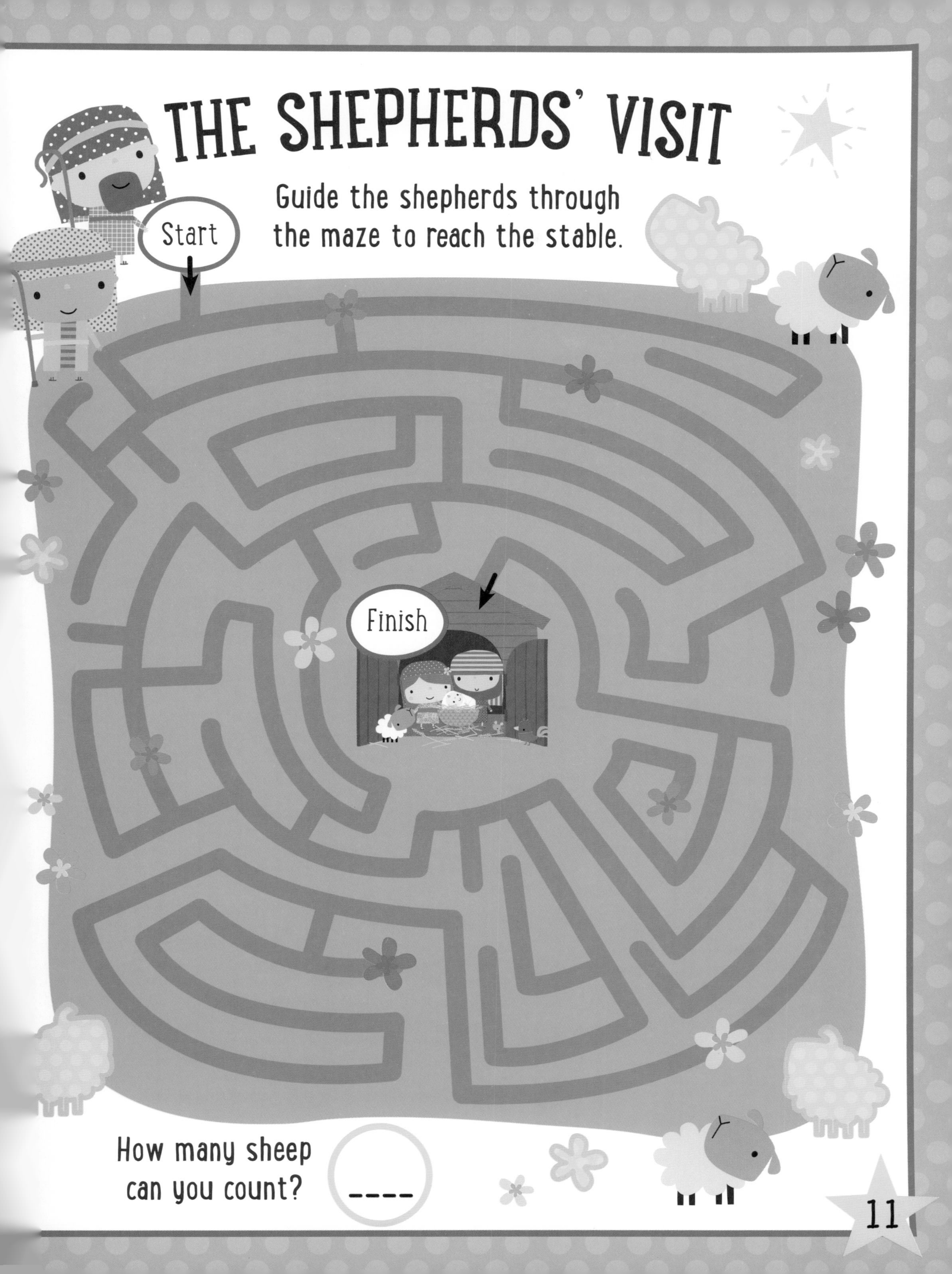

How many sheep can you count? ____

STARRY SEARCH

Jesus

star

Three wise men learn of Jesus by reading the stars. Find these six starry words below.

Joseph

stable

manger

Mary

j	o	s	e	p	h	m
e	p	i	o	t	j	a
s	m	a	r	y	d	n
u	r	m	k	b	f	g
s	t	a	r	p	m	e
d	u	r	y	z	j	r
s	t	a	b	l	e	o

FOLLOW THE STAR

Help the wise men find the baby Jesus
by stickering the golden squares
and following the path of stars.

Start →

→ Finish

GLORIOUS GIFTS

The wise men bring gifts for Jesus. Join the dots and add stickers to find out what they are.

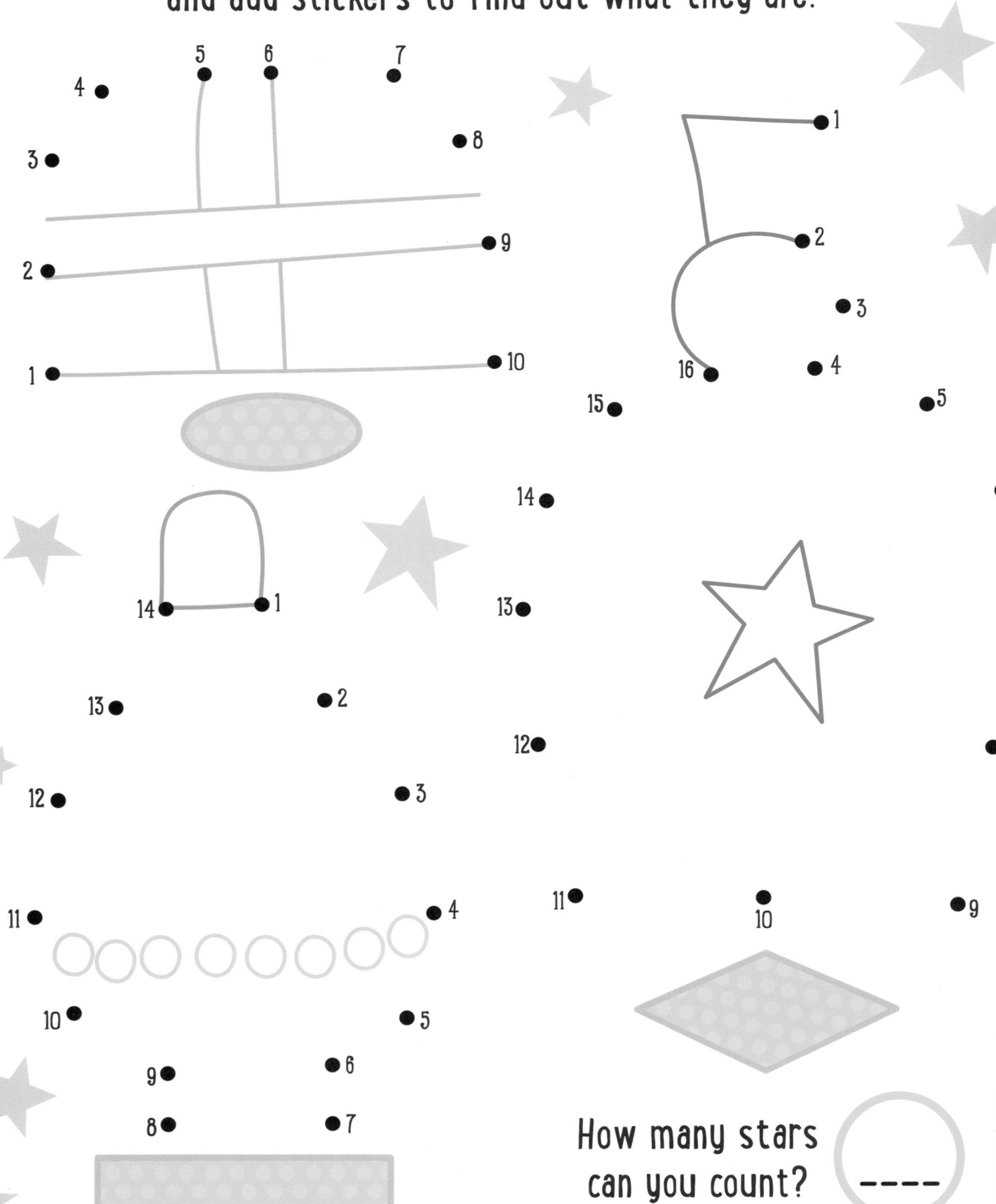

How many stars can you count? ----

PRETTY PATTERNS

Use colour and stickers to complete the Nativity patterns.

JOYFUL JIGSAW

Find the missing stickers to complete the Christmas scene.

SPREAD THE WORD

Press out and complete the card,
and then give it to a friend.

GOODWILL TO ALL

Press out and complete the gift tags.

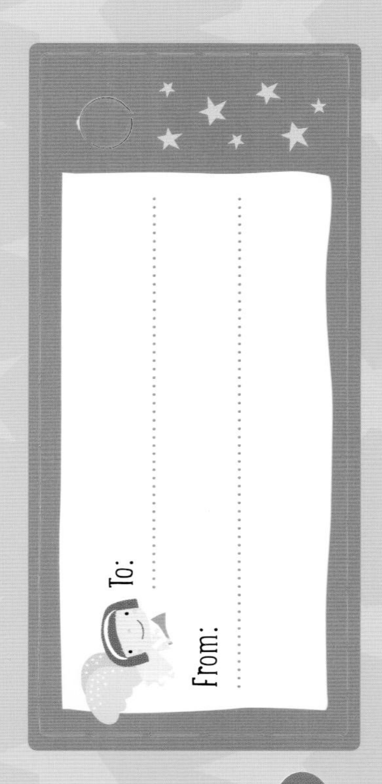

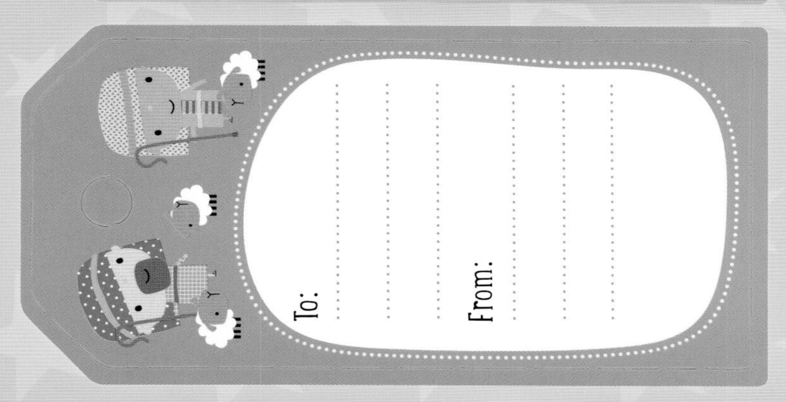

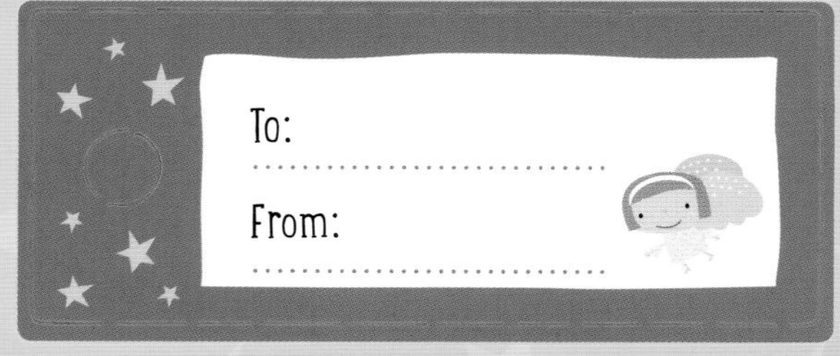

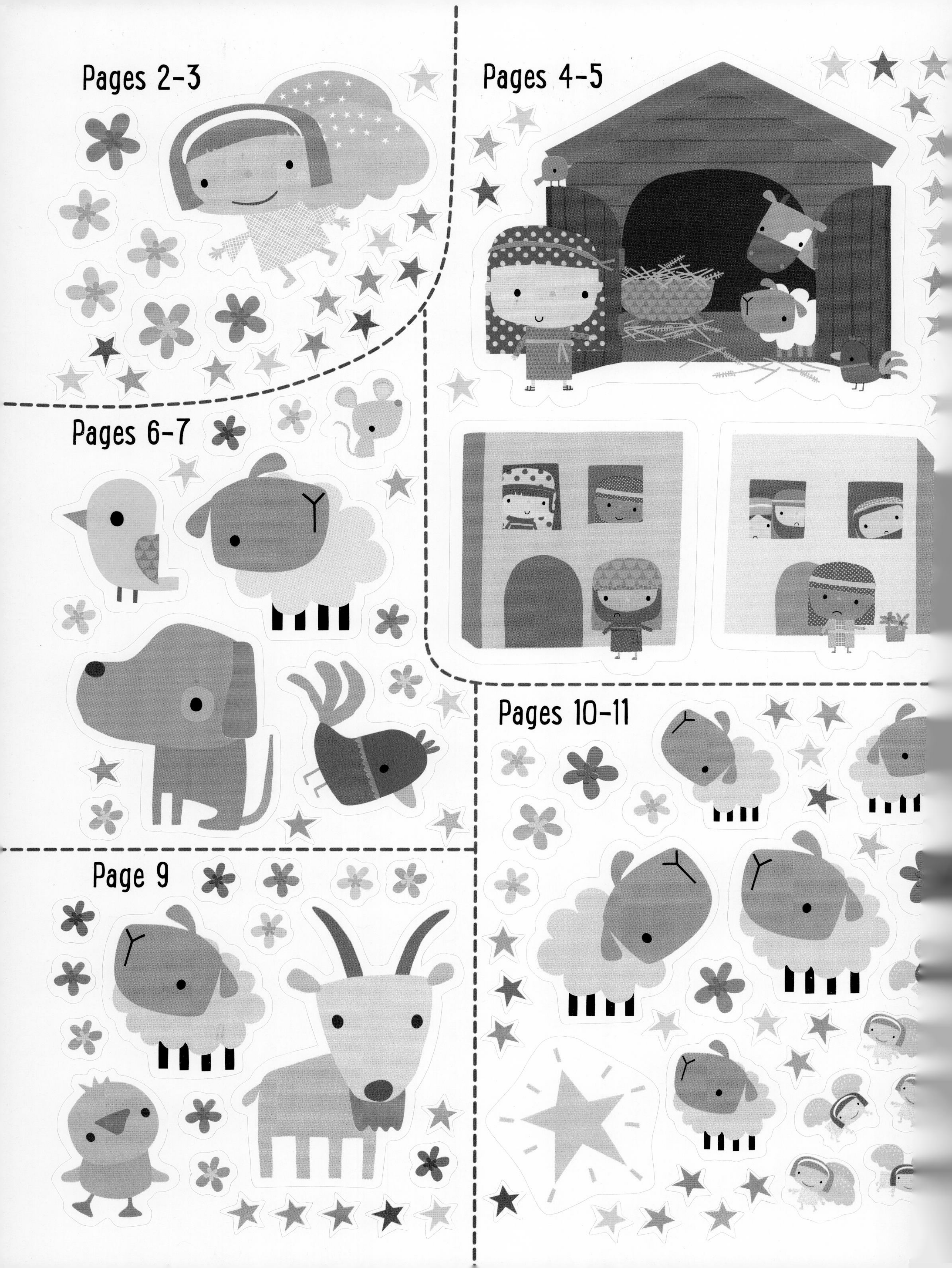

Pages 2-3
Pages 4-5
Pages 6-7
Page 9
Pages 10-11

Page 13
Pages 14-15
gold
frankincense
myrrh
Page 16
Extra stickers